Out-of-This-World Careers for Little Big Dreamers

THE SPACES YOU'LL GO

By Rachael Mann

Illustrations by Nacho Huizar

The Spaces You'll Go
© 2019 by Rachael Mann

Published 2019 by Bolígrafo Books
An imprint of Grafo House Publishing
Guadalajara, Jalisco, Mexico
grafohouse.com

In association with Jaquith Creative, a literary and
creative agency; Bothell, Washington, USA
jaquithcreative.com

ISBN 978-1-949791-25-9
ebook ISBN 978-1-949791-26-6

Also available in e-book format. Bulk discounts
available for schools, public institutions, and events.
For more information, contact info@grafohouse.com

To contact the author, follow @RachaelEdu on social
media or visit her website, www.rachaelmann.co

To contact the illustrator, follow him on Instagram
@latte_studio or visit his website, nachohuizar.com

My name is Cas,
And this is Kanga Blue.
There's no better friend
Than a kangaroo!

We love to hop and jump and play
As we dream about what we'll be someday.

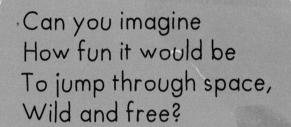

Can you imagine
How fun it would be
To jump through space,
Wild and free?

Space is the place
The stars all share.
It's beyond the birds
And clouds and air.

We might pilot a spaceship or fly a drone
To so many places we could call home.

We'll explore the planets and asteroids too,
And find fun spaces to walk or hop through.

We can dig on Titan, one of Saturn's moons,
And learn about the lakes and hills and dunes.

We'll fly to the workshop
Over on Mars
And build our own
Flying space cars!

We can take a ride
To the shiny Space Station
And work with scientists
From every nation.

We'll experiment with gravity.
Look at me spin!
Help sick people get better
With the right medicine.

We'll design spacesuits
For a fashion show:
Clothes that protect us
When we're on the go.

Fruits and vegetables
Can grow anywhere
With water, nutrients,
And lots of care.

SPACE FARMER

Then we'll zoom out to see
Jupiter's biggest storm.
How fast are its winds?
And how did it form?

We might map its moons:
Ganymede is one,
Then Callisto, Europa,
And Io, what fun!

CARTOGRAPHER.

People will need
Safe places to stay:
Fresh air, clean water,
And room to play.

We can build "green" homes
And learn to waste less.
Recycle what we use;
Garbage makes a big mess.

Environmentalist

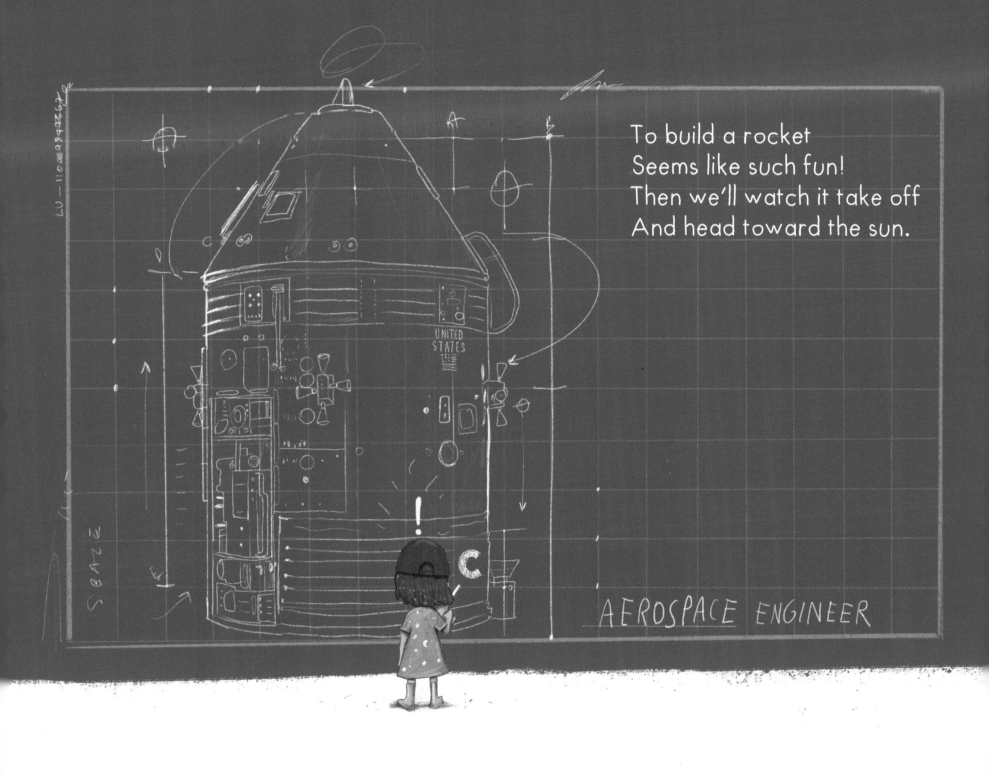

To build a rocket
Seems like such fun!
Then we'll watch it take off
And head toward the sun.

AEROSPACE ENGINEER

We'll calculate orbits
Both solar and lunar
Using computers
So work gets done sooner.

COMPUTER
PROGRAMMER

We'll invent new machines,
Robots, or drones,
Or ways of constructing
Cool space homes.

The sky is big
Like the dreams in my head.
But wait! It's so late.
It's time for bed.

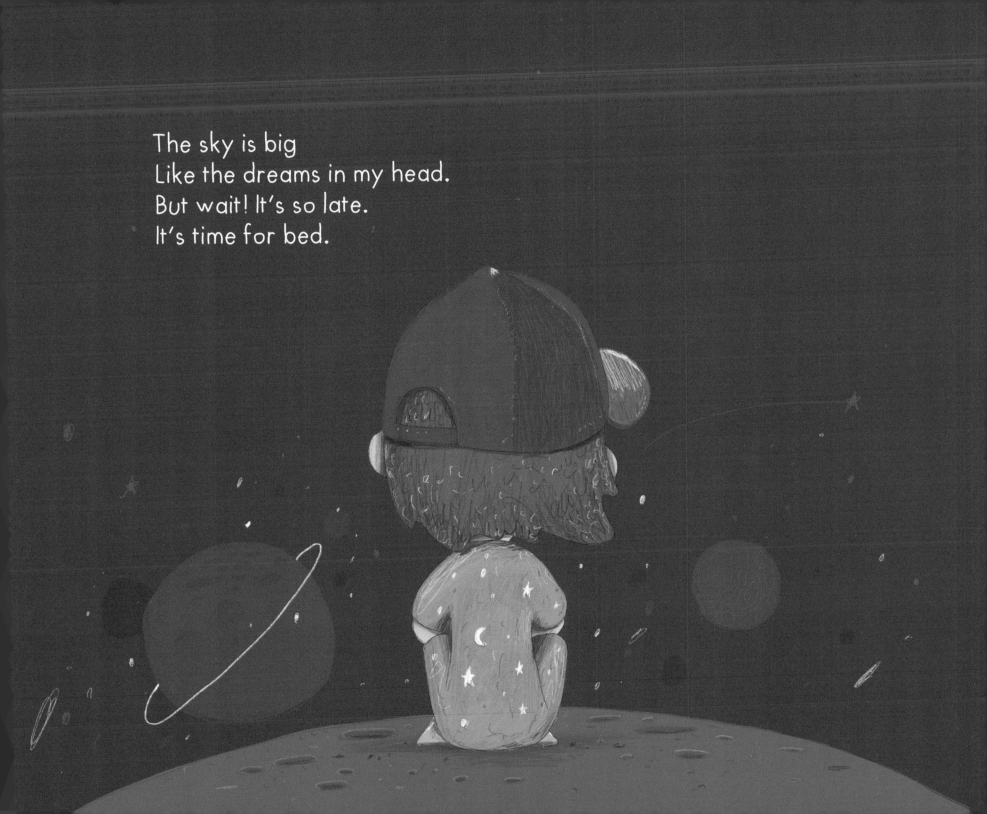

Oh, the spaces you'll go
And the places you'll see;
So much that you'll do
And so much that you'll be.

The sky's not the limit;
It's only the start.
There is a future in space
And you'll play a part.

Think big and dream bigger
And just do your best.
There are spaces you'll go,
But for now, just rest!

DEAR PARENTS, TEACHERS, AND LIBRARIANS,

The characters in this book, Cas (short for the constellation Cassiopeia) and her sidekick Kanga Blue (stuffed toy by day, robot by night) dream of the exciting things they may someday do that are related to space exploration. These careers exist now, on Earth, but their applications could change dramatically as current space initiatives open the universe up even more.

This lighthearted adventure through seventeen space-related careers is designed to encourage children's interest in Science, Technology, Engineering, and Math, often known as STEM. But even more importantly, it is meant to empower kids to believe that they can do and be anything. Dreams always come before reality, and when you encourage your little dreamers to look beyond the limits of the planet we call home, you are expanding their horizons to see opportunities and occupations that don't even exist yet.

Our world needs dreamers, explorers, and innovators, people who ask, "How can we?" That is why it is so important to give kids the freedom to discover what they <u>love</u>, what they <u>are curious about</u>, what they <u>do well</u>, and what the world <u>needs</u>. At the intersection of these points lies their destiny.

Thank you for using the drawing power of space to get your kids interested in STEM at a young age. I hope this book serves as a launchpad to inspire wonder about the universe we live in, yet are just beginning to understand. For bonus resources, please visit www.rachaelmann.co and follow the hashtags #ReadytoLaunch and #SpacesYoullGo on social media.

Dream big, aim high... space awaits!

Rachael Mann

Glossary

AEROSPACE ENGINEER
Flying is awesome, so I imagine and build new kinds of airplanes and spaceships.

ARCHITECT
I dream about amazing buildings, like houses and skyscrapers, and make blueprints to build them.

CARTOGRAPHER
I draw maps to help people find their way in new places.

CIVIL ENGINEER
I love to build! I design and build roads, bridges, airports, and more.

COMPUTER PROGRAMMER
I like computers, and I create computer programs to help people do their work better and faster.

DOCTOR
I love to help people who are sick or hurt feel better.

ENVIRONMENTALIST
I protect nature by helping people be smart and careful about how they live.

EXPLORER
I love new places! I try to find things no one else has seen before.

FASHION DESIGNER
I help design clothes, shoes, spacesuits, and other things people wear in space.

GEOLOGIST
I learn about what planets are made of and where they came from.

INVENTOR
I think about things no one has ever made, and then I figure out how to make them.

METEOROLOGIST
I look at the weather to know if it's going to be hot or cold, rainy or sunny.

PILOT
I fly airplanes, spaceships, and anything else that soars through the air.

ROBOTICS ENGINEER
I build robots because robots aren't just cool, they also help us in so many ways!

SCIENTIST
I learn about the world around me to know how things work and what they are made of.

SPACE FARMER
I grow fruits, vegetables, and plants on the Space Station or even other planets.

SPACE MECHANIC
I fix spaceships and other machines when they break down.

ABOUT THE AUTHOR

Rachael Mann is passionate about all things related to education, technology, and science. She is an "edufuturist" who believes in the importance of shaping the educational philosophies and spaces of today by looking toward the innovations of tomorrow. Rachael is a frequent keynote speaker at STEM-related events, and she speaks and writes about disruptive technology, education, and careers. She is the coauthor of "The Martians in Your Classroom", an educational title about integrating STEM in classrooms. Rachael holds an MA in educational leadership, and her undergraduate studies were in family and consumer sciences. She has fourteen years of classroom experience in a range of subjects, including child development, early childhood education, science, technology, and culinary courses. She serves on several national boards dedicated to ensuring that kids are future ready. She lives with her husband in Phoenix, Arizona and loves being the best aunt in the world to her eight nieces and nephews. Connect with Rachael on social media @RachaelEdu or visit her website, www.rachaelmann.co, to learn more about her work.

ABOUT THE ILLUSTRATOR

Nacho Zarate Huizar is a designer and illustrator from Oaxaca, Mexico. He loves design, details, branding, and visual storytelling in general. His clients include some of the largest firms in the world, and his work has been featured in numerous magazines, websites, and other publications. Nacho lives in Guadalajara, México with his wife Pau and their little big adventurer, Daniel. Every illustration in this book was inspired by their tiny daughter-to-be and the adoption journey they are on to bring her home. See more of Nacho's artwork at nachohuizar.com or follow him on Instagram @latte_studio.

CPSIA information can be obtained
at www.ICGtesting.com
Printed in the USA
LVHW011009171122
733292LV00008B/306

9 7 8 1 9 4 9 7 9 1 2 5 9